DOMENICO SCARLATTI
NINE SONATAS

Edited by Howard Ferguson

(The Kp-numbers refer to the possible chronological order proposed by Ralph Kirkpatrick in his important book, *Domenico Scarlatti*; Princeton 1953.)

THE ASSOCIATED BOARD OF
THE ROYAL SCHOOLS OF MUSIC

INTRODUCTION

Domenico Scarlatti (1685-1757)

Domenico Scarlatti, son of the Neapolitan opera composer Alessandro, was born in the same year as Bach and Handel. His early manhood was spent in various posts in Naples, Venice and Rome; then, at about the age of 34, he became *maestro* of the Portugese royal chapel, and harpsichord teacher to the King's eldest daughter, the Infanta Maria Barbara. On her marriage in 1728 to Fernando, heir to the Spanish throne, he moved with the rest of the Princess's entourage to Madrid, where he remained for the rest of his life.

Though he had composed vocal, instrumental, and operatic works while still in Italy, Scarlatti is known today almost entirely by the 555 harpsichord Sonatas (mostly in single-movement binary form) that he is thought to have written mainly after his arrival in the Iberian Peninsula. Strangely enough, none of the Sonatas has survived in autograph. Some seventy were published in London, Amsterdam and Paris between 1728 and Scarlatti's death; but the majority are known only through contemporary manuscript copies. The most important of these are contained in two collections: (1) the 15 sumptuously-bound volumes that belonged to the Queen of Spain (now in Venice, Biblioteca Nationale Marciana, 9770-84); and (2) a similar though not identical set of 15 volumes, whose original owner is unknown (Parma, Conservatorio di Musica Arrigo Boito, AG 31406-20).[1]

The present texts are taken from the Parma MSS, with the exception of Nos.3 & 4 from the Venice MSS, and No.7 from the 'Worgan MS' (British Library, Add. MS.31553). Since there are no dynamics in the originals and almost no marks of articulation (slurs and staccatos), these have been added by the editor. The full words *forte* and *piano* here indicate the broad contrasts obtainable on a two-manual harpsichord, and hence the general dynamic level of a passage, section or complete piece. The remaining signs (*f, mf, mp, p, cresc., dim.*, ⎯⎯⎯ ⎯⎯⎯) show the type of gradations that a pianist (as distinct from a harpsichordist) might make within these limits. The articulation, which is of the utmost importance in Scarlatti, is such as might have been used by one of his contemporaries. A suggested interpretation of each ornament is shown above or below the stave at its first appearance in every piece. Note, however, that Scarlatti's ornamentation depends more on its context than on the particular sign used: so a single ornament is sometimes interpreted in two different ways, and two different ornaments in a single way. This is intentional. An editorial metronome mark has been added at the end of each piece; it should be understood, however, that it is neither authoritative nor binding. Numbered footnotes are concerned with textual matters and lettered footnotes with interpretation.

HOWARD FERGUSON
Cambridge 1987

---

[1]Complete facsimile edition, based mainly on the Parma MSS: Domenico Scarlatti, *Complete Keyboard Works*, vols.1-18, ed. Ralph Kirkpatrick; Johnson Reprint Corporation, New York & London 1972. Complete modern edition, based mainly on the Venice MSS: Domenico Scarlatti, *Sonates*, vols.1-11, ed. Kenneth Gilbert; Heugel, Paris 1971-84.

NINE SONATAS

Sonata in C

Kp.159

SCARLATTI

1) B.16 is missing in the source; but see bb.53-55.

(b) Bb.58-59: players may care to substitute the following editorial r.h. part, by analogy with bb.19-20, which Scarlatti would probably have written if the high G had been available on most harpsichords:-

Sonata in F minor
Kp.462

1) Bb.2-3: the r.h. slurs are in the source. The remainder are editorial.

Sonata in C

Kp.86

1) B.43: the source has a single barline without repeat-signs.

2) B.44: the source has a single barline without repeat-signs.

3) B.81: the source has D.C. following the double-bar.

[♩ = c.112]

Sonata in G

Kp.103

1) The 8-note slurs in bb.5-6, 10-11, 27-28 & 38-39, 6-note slurs in bb.12-15, 4-note slurs in bb.19 & 47, and 2-note slurs in bb.17-18, 20, 45-46 and 48 are in the source.

2) B.21, r.h. note 3: the source has C, not D.

3) B.48, l.h. upper line, note 4: the source has A; but see the more probable bb.18, 20 & 46.

4) B.52: the source has D.C. following the double-bar.

Sonata in B minor

Kp.87

1) B.10, l.h. lower note 1: the source has A, not F(sharp).

2) B.35, l.h. note 2: the source has crotchet E, not quaver.

3) Bb.37-38: in the source the r.h., except for note 1, is a 3rd too high. (Longo's emendation is nonsensical.)

[♩ = c.62]

Sonata in F sharp

Kp.318

1) B.7, r.h. lower line: in the source the final C(sharp) comes a beat earlier; but see the more probable b.25.

[♩ = c.116]

Sonata in F sharp minor

Kp.142

1) B.51, r.h. upper notes 3-4: in the source the F(sharps) are tied; but not in b.53.

2) B.51, l.h. beat 1: the F(sharp) is dotted in the source.

3) B.53, l.h. beat 2: the F(sharp) is dotted in the source.

[♩. = c.100]

Sonata in E minor

Kp.402

1) B.14: the r.h. ornament is on note 2 in the source, not note 3.

Sonata in E

Kp.531

1) B.6, l.h. note 6: the source has C(sharp), not A; but see the more probable b.2.

AB 1971

AB 1971

[♩. = c.104]

Processed and printed by
Halstan & Co. Ltd., Amersham, Bucks., England

THEMATIC INDEX